This Walker book belongs to:

ANCIENT EGYPT

TALES OF GODS AND PHARAOHS

RETOLD AND
ILLUSTRATED BY
MARCIA WILLIAMS

In the Beginning, there was only

the deep,

dark

water

of

Nun.

Then out of the water rose an island.
On the island stood Ra, the Shining One.
Ra was the first god to stand on the land of Egypt.

Ra had a Secret Name, which gave him the power to bring anything into being with just a word or a glance!

First Ra brought forth Shu, the god of air, and Tefnut, the goddess of rain.

Then came Geb, the god of the earth, and Nut, the goddess of the sky.

Then Ra named Hapi, the great River Nile that flows through Egypt.

After this Ra gave life to men and women and all the things on Earth, both great and small.

Then Ra took on the shape of a man and became the first Pharaoh of Egypt. And every year the River Nile rose up and flooded the fields to help the crops grow. So there was peace and plenty in the reign of Ra.

And the cat named Rami was Ra's favourite. And to him Ra gave many lives!

ISIS AND THE COBRA

In the reign of Ra, Nut and Geb gave birth to the clever goddess, Isis. She married Osiris, her brother, the likely heir to Ra's crown.

As time passed Ra's human form grew old.

Yet he still did not want to give Osiris his crown.

So Isis used her magic powers against him.

When Ra dribbled on the ground, Isis formed the damp sand into a cobra.

The next day, the light of Ra's eye fell on the serpent and gave it life!

The cobra reared up and bit Ra — he cried out in agony.

The pain grew like fire in Ra's limbs and his eyes slowly dimmed.

Isis offered to heal him if he told her his Secret Name. Ra spoke many names, but not his name of power.

Finally, the pain grew unbearable and Ra let his Secret Name pass to Isis. Isis bade the serpent's venom leave him and Ra was at peace.

Once his Secret Name was shared with Isis, Ra could no longer reign on Earth.
He took his place in the heavens and travelled across the sky in the likeness of the sun.
He became known as Amen Ra.

At night he passed through the underworld, called the Duat. As dawn rose he returned to
the heavens taking with him the spirits of the dead who had won a place in his heavenly kingdom.

It's best not to eat each other.

The above activities are recommended by our great Pharaoh Osiris and his queen.

But the lion ate my rabbit, O Pharaoh.

On earth, Osiris became Pharaoh of Egypt and Isis his queen. They cared well for their people, teaching them many things — including not to eat each other. They also built a great temple for Amen Ra in their new city of Thebes.

In Egypt cats eat ducks – ducks don't eat cats!

Nile crocodiles are dangerous!

The Egyptian people fear them.

Crocs eat anything – even cats.

Meow, another life gone ... seven to go.

Burp!

SETH THE EVIL ONE

Life, health and power.

O beloved Pharaoh.

Death, sickness and weakness, O unbeloved Pharaoh.

Everyone loved Pharaoh Osiris – except his younger brother, Seth.
He wanted to be pharaoh and planned to steal Osiris's crown.

Jolly good show.

It gets better!

Seth invited Osiris to a banquet with some of his wicked friends.
After the feasting a casket was carried in ... a gift from Seth to anyone who fitted inside it!

After cats, the wisest of Ra's creatures is mankind.

They soon decide to take up farming.

They grow crops along the banks of the Nile.

Wheat   Barley   Figs   Pomegranates   Grapes   Vegetables

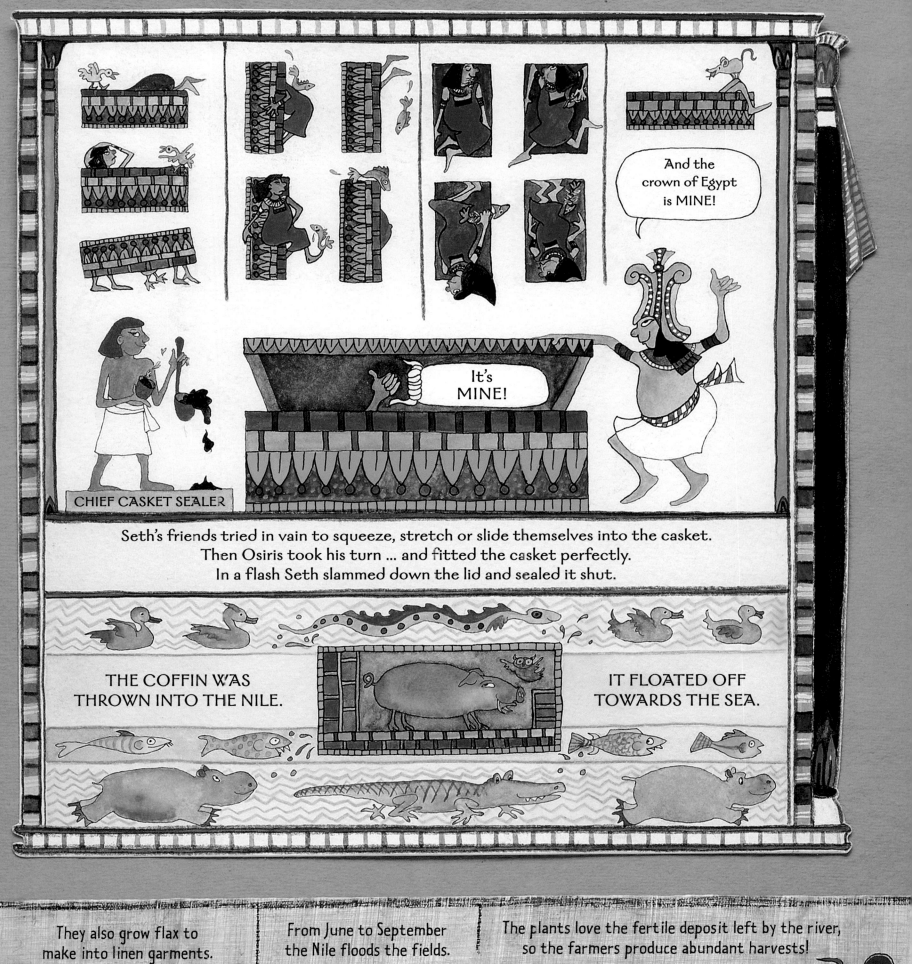

CHIEF CASKET SEALER

Seth's friends tried in vain to squeeze, stretch or slide themselves into the casket.
Then Osiris took his turn ... and fitted the casket perfectly.
In a flash Seth slammed down the lid and sealed it shut.

THE COFFIN WAS
THROWN INTO THE NILE.

IT FLOATED OFF
TOWARDS THE SEA.

They also grow flax to make into linen garments.

From June to September the Nile floods the fields.

The plants love the fertile deposit left by the river, so the farmers produce abundant harvests!

Poor, brave Isis set out once more to search for her husband's body.

After weeks of searching she found all but one part of Osiris's body.

To protect Osiris from Seth, Isis buried Osiris in thirteen different places!

So finally, the spirit of Osiris passed into the Duat, where he became King of the Dead ...

while his wicked brother, Seth, became Pharaoh of Egypt, which was more than he deserved!

Wild cats keep the rats and mice from the grain stores.

Cats soon become tame.

They are Ancient Egypt's favourite pet – no home is complete without one ... or two!

HORUS THE AVENGER!

"We don't want that nasty Horus stealing you, do we?"

"We'll just have to kill him, won't we my precious?!"

Seth was Pharaoh of Egypt, but the crown really belonged to his nephew, Horus.

Seth decided to kill him, as he'd killed Osiris, Horus's father.

"You are safe from your nasty Uncle Seth here."

"I wouldn't bet on it."

Horus was still a child and guarded by his mother, Isis, on a floating island.

One night, as the island bumped against the banks of the Nile, Seth crossed onto it.

He took the shape of a scorpion and crawled into Horus's room where he stung him.

A cat is often taken hunting instead of a dog — MEOWEEE!

A cat is better at retrieving ducks and fish from the marshes.

Before long the Ancient Egyptians had made the cat a god!

The most famous cat goddess is Bastet.

All night Horus screamed as Isis tried to heal him, but by morning he appeared dead.

The wise god Thoth comforted Isis and reassured her that she would see her son again.

Horus had passed into the Duat, but only so that his father, Osiris, could prepare him to fight Seth and avenge his death.

Horus remained with Osiris until he became a man and was ready to meet Seth in battle.

Or Bast, as she is known when she takes the body of a woman.

Bastet is the goddess of fertility and protector of children.

The temples of Bastet are full of pampered cats.

Warning! You can be put to death for killing a CAT!

Amen Ra took Horus to the land of the living in his sacred boat.

Seth was ready and waiting. He charged at Horus and aimed a bolt of fire into his eyes.

Horus was blinded and unable to fight back — he roared with pain and anger.

It was many weeks before Horus regained his sight and could go after Seth again.

Sekhmet is also a cat goddess.

She is a lion and fiercer than Bastet.

Sekhmet protects the pharaohs.

She expects large offerings – or else!

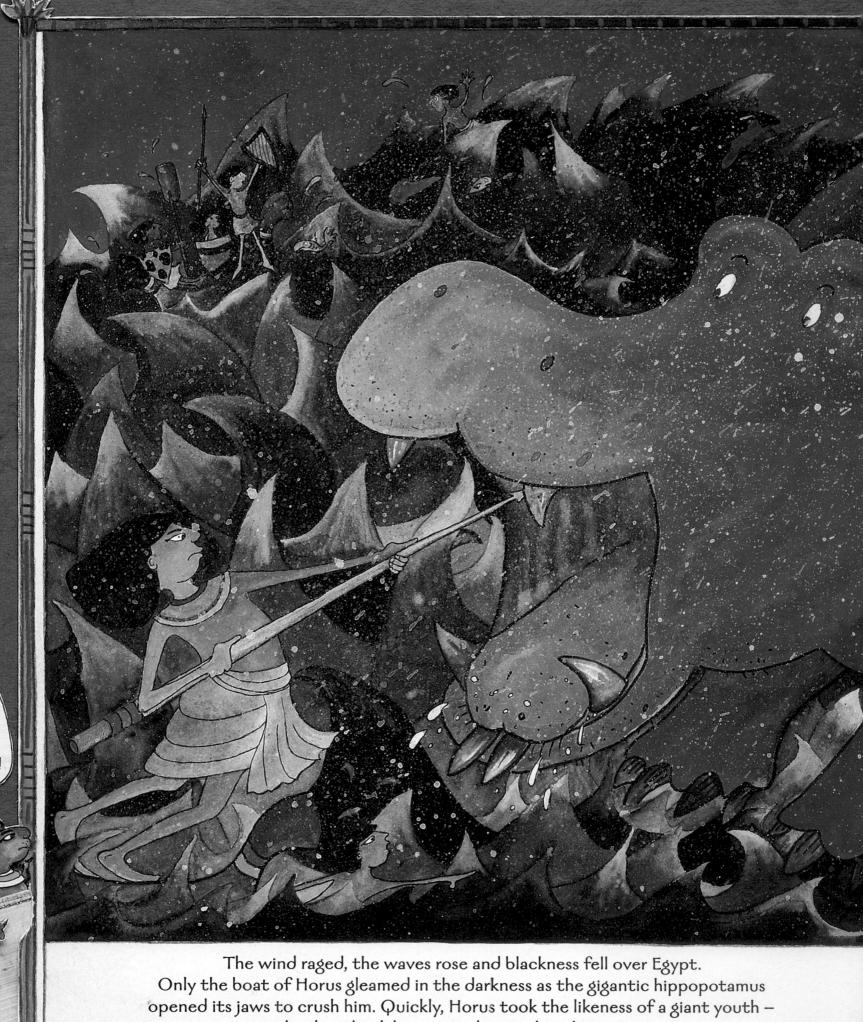

The wind raged, the waves rose and blackness fell over Egypt.
Only the boat of Horus gleamed in the darkness as the gigantic hippopotamus
opened its jaws to crush him. Quickly, Horus took the likeness of a giant youth —
he drew back his arm and cast a long harpoon.

Even Pharaoh Zoser was satisfied with his tomb! It was a beautiful step pyramid built at Saqqara, on the edge of the desert. The outside was covered in white limestone that glinted in the sunlight. At night it looked like a stairway to the Heavens.

Inside, wonderful etchings and carvings decorated the walls leading to Zoser's burial chamber. Never before had such a large stone monument been built, not even for the great god Ra, creator of all Egypt. For as long as it stood, Pharaoh Zoser would be remembered, which made him very, very happy.

Horus threw it with such force that it travelled through the roof of Seth's mouth and into his brain. The red hippopotamus sank dead into the Nile, the darkness vanished and the people of Egypt rejoiced at the victory of Horus the Avenger. Peace came to Egypt and Horus was crowned Pharaoh.

I'll give him revenge!

Amen Ra and Thoth went to the palace of Thutmose
and cast a spell upon the household, so that every living thing slept.

Then Ra entered the chamber of Ahmes, bathing the room in light.
As he placed himself beside her the couch rose up, so that it was neither on the earth nor in the heavens.
Ra held a sweet perfume to Ahmes's nostrils and the breath of life passed into her.

Some children may have tops, dolls,
toy weapons and the
odd pull-along animal.

Swimming is also popular...
especially with the crocodiles.

Ball games, wrestling, racing
and dancing are all good fun!

After nine months, a baby girl named Hatshepsut was born to Ahmes. All Egypt rejoiced.

Once again a great sleep fell upon the palace while Ra visited the child.
He took with him Hathor, the goddess of love, and her seven daughters who weave the web of life
for all newborns. Ra gave Hatshepsut the kiss of power, while the Hathors wove the golden web
of her life so that she would be a great queen. And all the while the palace slept.

School is not so popular!

A boy's ears are
in his backside.

But if you want to grow up
to be a scribe, doctor, lawyer,
priest or vizier you have to go.

We don't even
want to grow up!

Most girls are educated at home. Not many learn
to read or write. Some girls become dancers,
singers or musicians. Only a few become scribes.

As Hatshepsut grew, she took her place beside her earthly father, Pharaoh Thutmose, and learned how to care for his people.

Then the time came for Hatshepsut to be crowned Pharaoh of all Egypt.
Hatshepsut and Amen Ra were both very happy, for they had always known that this was her destiny.
Pharaoh Hatshepsut was a wise and powerful ruler and Egypt flourished under the rule of its queen!

The Ancient Egyptians marry young, so childhood is short.

Soon children become parents.

It is the duty of children to honour and look after their parents ... and their pet CATS!!!

PRINCE THUTMOSE AND THE SPHINX

After the death of Queen Hatshepsut her stepson, Thutmose, became pharaoh followed by his grandson, Amenhotep.

Pharaoh Amenhotep had many sons, but his favourite was named Thutmose, after his grandfather.

The other brothers were jealous of Thutmose and didn't want him to inherit the crown.

They were often unkind and tried hard to turn their father against him.

Thutmose would escape from their taunts by going hunting.

Cats are Egypt's greatest wonder, then comes the River Nile.

It gives us many gifts and even carries the stones used for pyramid building.

It also provides the water for the people who help to build the pyramids.

They live in villages that grow up close to the building site.

One day, when the court was at Memphis for a festival, Thutmose and two companions left to hunt gazelles in the desert. They rode until midday, when the heat forced them to stop and rest.

Unable to forget his brothers' jealousy, Thutmose was too unhappy to rest, so he decided to leave his sleeping companions and explore the great pyramids of Giza.

Secret rooms are hidden deep inside the pyramids to keep out tomb raiders.

False chamber

Warning statues of gods and sphinxes are built outside the pyramids.

Roar!

Nice kitty.

Some robbers still plunder the treasure meant for the pharaoh in his next life.

I'm rich!

May they grow rat-tails, mouse-whiskers and fish-scales!

I'm transformed.

The pyramids were vast, but what fascinated Thutmose was the head of a stone sphinx, just sticking out of the sand. He thought it must be a likeness of the god Harmichis, so he prayed that his brothers might leave him in peace. Then, falling asleep in the shade of the great sphinx, Thutmose had the strangest dream.

Death shall come on swift wings to him that disturbs the peace of the King.

Death shall come on swift wing

THE SECOND
MUMMIFORM
SARCOPHAGUS

After seventy days Tutankhamen's body was placed in a huge tomb in The Valley of the Kings.
On the outside of the tomb was inscribed a terrible curse, warning all those
that dared to enter the tomb not to disturb the peace of the young pharaoh.

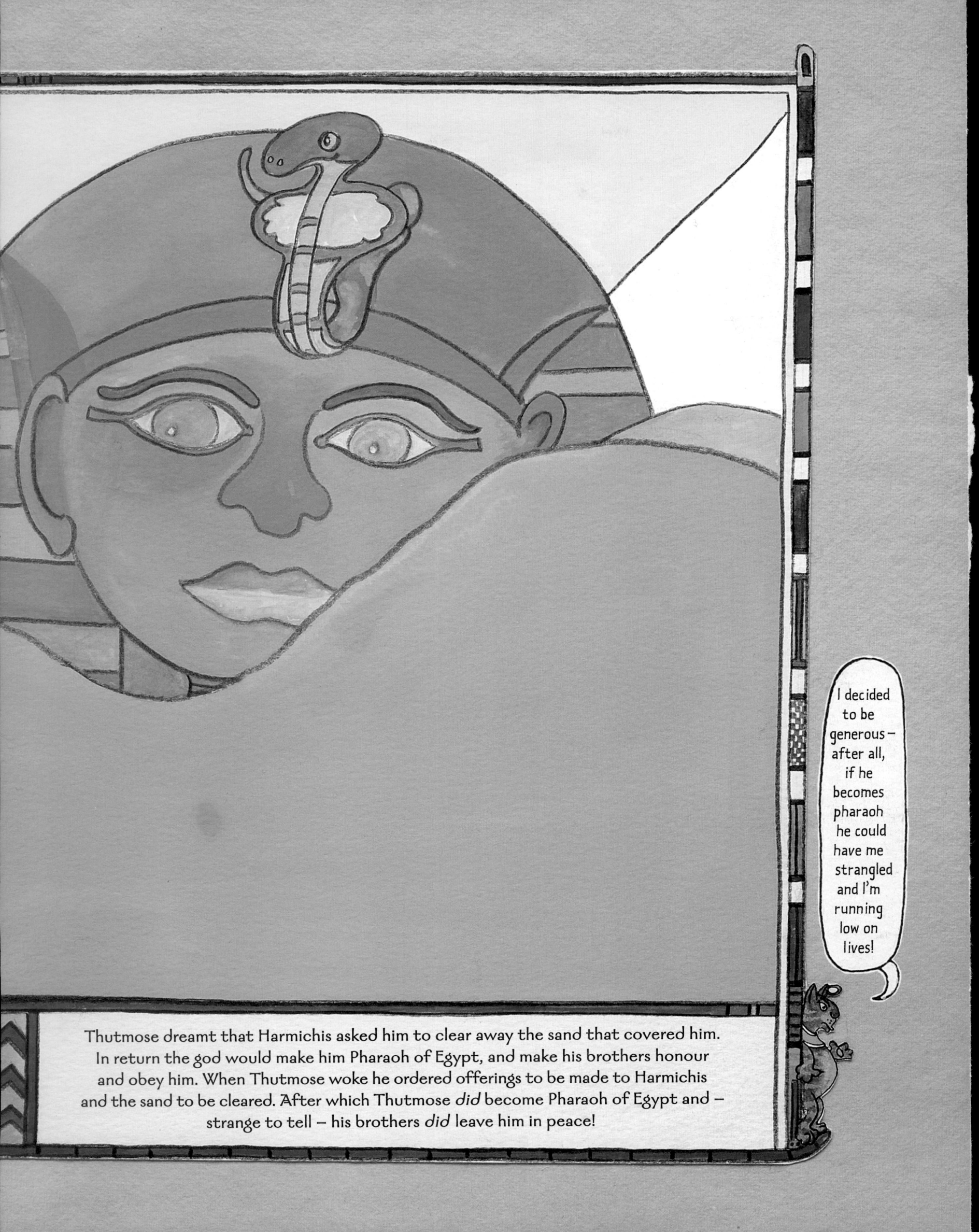

Thutmose dreamt that Harmichis asked him to clear away the sand that covered him. In return the god would make him Pharaoh of Egypt, and make his brothers honour and obey him. When Thutmose woke he ordered offerings to be made to Harmichis and the sand to be cleared. After which Thutmose *did* become Pharaoh of Egypt and — strange to tell — his brothers *did* leave him in peace!

The tomb was filled with a vast feast of treasures, including 130 walking sticks, to aid Pharaoh Tutankhamen's journey to the Next Life. Maybe the richness of the treasures was also a way of thanking the young pharaoh for reinstating the Egyptians' ancient beliefs in their many wonderful gods.

THE THIRD
MUMMIFORM
SARCOPHAGUS

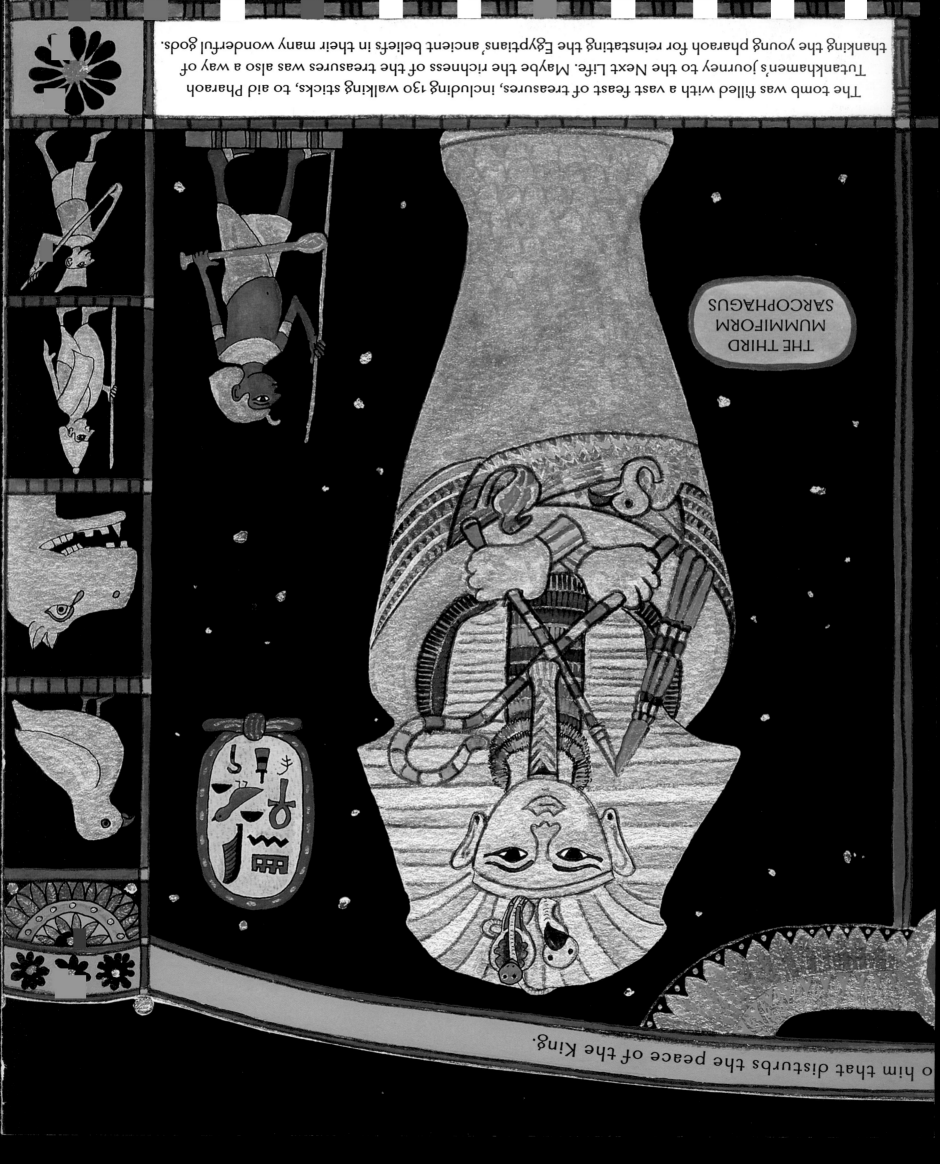

o him that disturbs the peace of the King.

Death shall come on swift wings to him that disturbs the peace of the King.

So when Akhenaten died and his son, Tutankhaten, became pharaoh, they were delighted... even though he was a frail nine-year-old child who walked with a stick.

With the help of his vizier, Ay, Tutankhaten tried to uphold his dad's beliefs, but he soon saw how unhappy it made his people.

So, after two years, he changed his name to Tutankhamen in honour of Amen Ra and reinstated the priests and temples.

He threw lavish parties in honour of Amen Ra and gradually began to win the hearts of the old priests and his people.

Then, when he was only nineteen years old, Tutankhamen had a fall and fractured his thigh. Frail from birth and also suffering from malaria, the young pharaoh quickly weakened and died.

You can open the flaps now, I expect you'll be cursed anyway!

When the carpet was unrolled and Cleopatra popped out,
Caesar was captivated and agreed to rid her of Ptolemy.

In the civil war that followed Ptolemy was killed
and Cleopatra became the sole ruler of Egypt!

Cleopatra began to think she might rule
the world and went with Caesar to Rome,
along with their baby Caesarion.

The couple's growing ambition shocked the
Roman senators and after months of plotting,
they assassinated Caesar.

Cleopatra fled back to Egypt, where she set about
restoring her power and her country's wealth.

With Caesar dead, Cleopatra needed another Roman ally to prevent Egypt from becoming part of the Roman Empire. So Cleopatra dressed herself as the goddess Isis and set sail for Tarsus to meet Mark Antony, one of Rome's new leaders.

Like Caesar before him, Antony immediately forgot his Roman wife and went back to Egypt with Cleopatra. For many years Antony abandoned Rome for Cleopatra, until finally the Roman leader, Octavius, declared war on them.

For months they fought and it seemed that neither side would ever win.

Until one day, in the midst of a sea battle, Cleopatra and her navy suddenly turned and fled, leaving Octavius triumphant.

Antony sailed back to Egypt a broken man. Beaten in battle and betrayed by Cleopatra, he fell on his sword.

Octavius was delighted and couldn't wait to parade Cleopatra through the streets of all the cities she had ruled, as his slave.

I must return to Amen Ra.

If he'll have you!

First, I'd like to remind you of the brilliance of we Ancient Egyptians.

Boring!

In about 1500 BC we invented glass making ... probably!

A glass fish

In about 1160 BC we drew the world's first known maps ... definitely!

The Queen of Egypt would never submit to such a fate and managed to escape to her tomb.
There she killed herself with the help of an asp whose bite, she believed, would make her immortal.
Maybe she was right, for with her death Egypt became part of the Roman Empire and
so Cleopatra will always be remembered as the last of Egypt's great pharaohs.

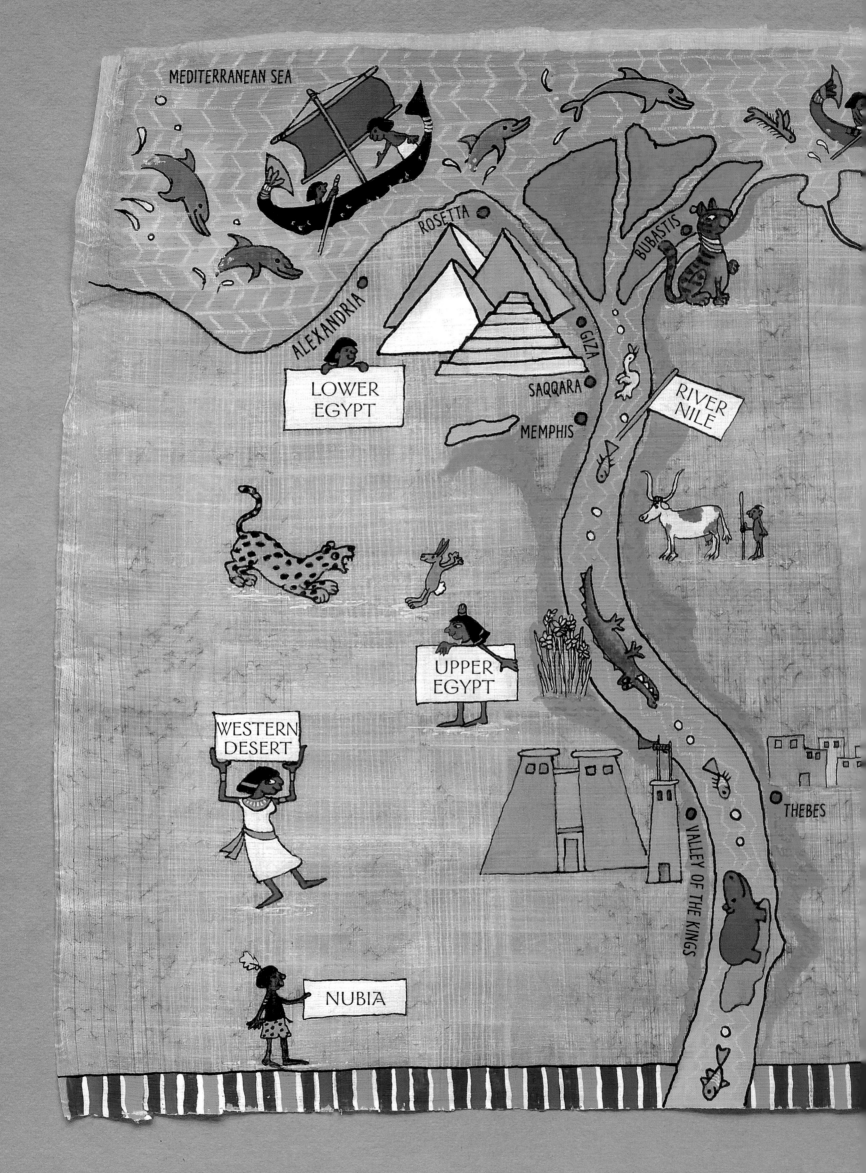

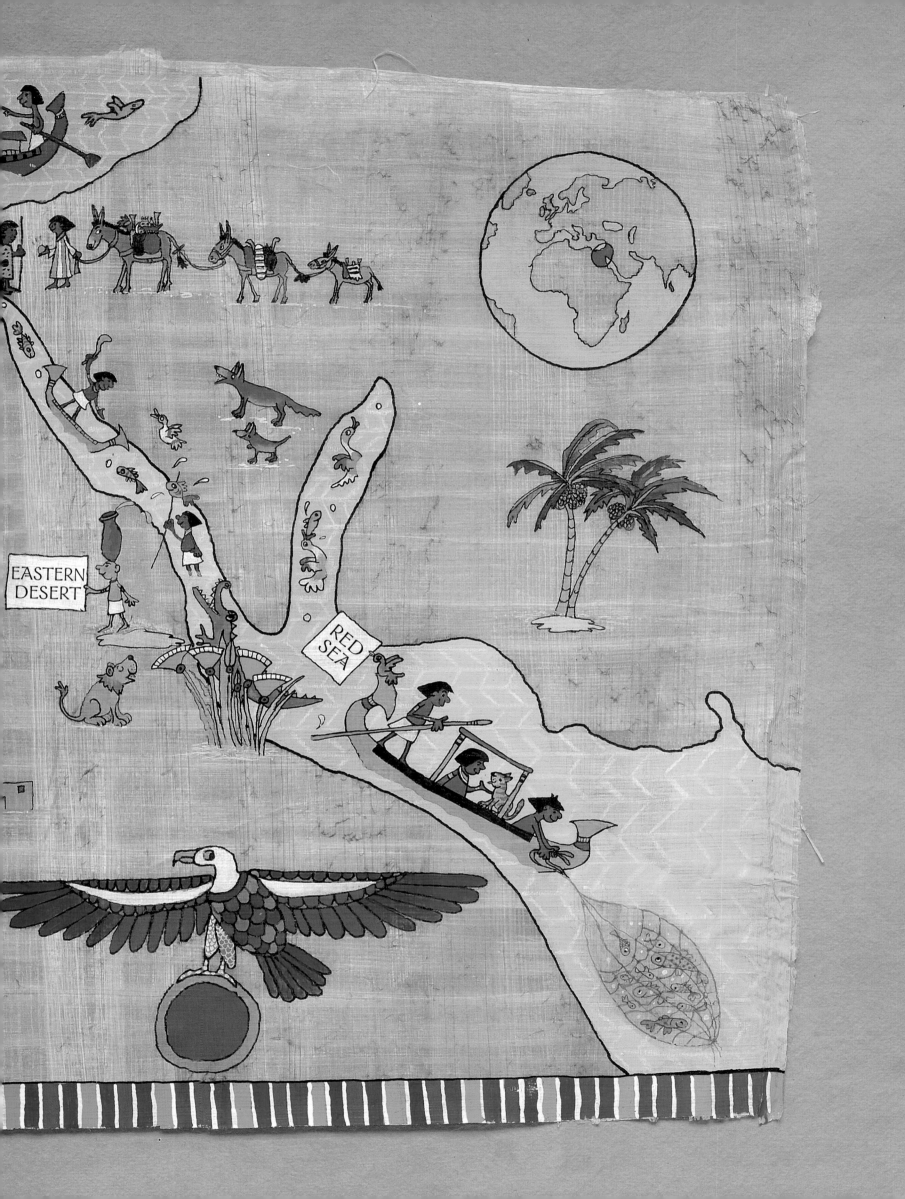

EASTERN
DESERT

RED
SEA

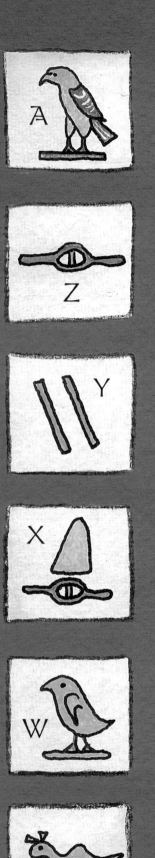

A

B

C

D

HOUSE

Z

Y

X

W

V

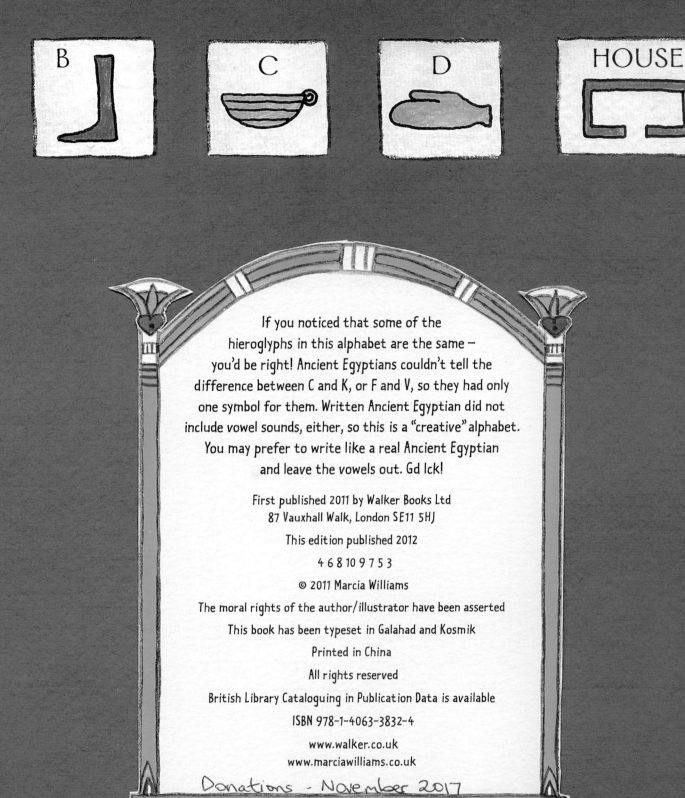

If you noticed that some of the hieroglyphs in this alphabet are the same – you'd be right! Ancient Egyptians couldn't tell the difference between C and K, or F and V, so they had only one symbol for them. Written Ancient Egyptian did not include vowel sounds, either, so this is a "creative" alphabet. You may prefer to write like a real Ancient Egyptian and leave the vowels out. Gd lck!

First published 2011 by Walker Books Ltd
87 Vauxhall Walk, London SE11 5HJ

This edition published 2012

4 6 8 10 9 7 5 3

© 2011 Marcia Williams

The moral rights of the author/illustrator have been asserted

This book has been typeset in Galahad and Kosmik

Printed in China

British Library Cataloguing in Publication Data is available

ISBN 978-1-4063-3832-4

www.walker.co.uk
www.marciawilliams.co.uk

Donations - November 2017

U

T

S

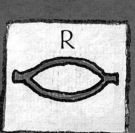

R

BOAT

WATER

E

F

G

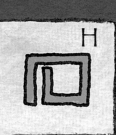

H

I

J

K

L

M

N

It has come from beginning to end.

Meow!

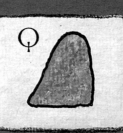

FIRE

Q

P

O

Marcia Williams

With her distinctive cartoon-strip style, lively text and brilliant wit, Marcia Williams brings to life some of the world's all-time favourite stories and some colourful historical characters. Her hilarious retellings and clever observations will have children laughing out loud and coming back for more!

ISBN 978-1-4063-3523-1

ISBN 978-1-4063-2997-1

ISBN 978-1-4063-2610-9

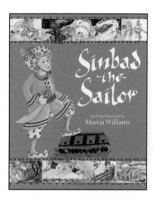

ISBN 978-1-4063-1944-6

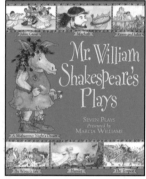

ISBN 978-1-4063-2334-4

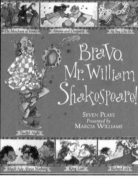

ISBN 978-1-4063-2335-1

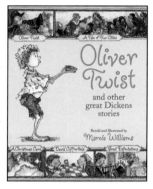

ISBN 978-1-4063-0563-0

ISBN 978-1-4063-0562-3

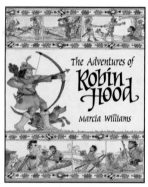

ISBN 978-1-4063-1137-2

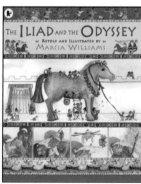

ISBN 978-1-4063-1866-1

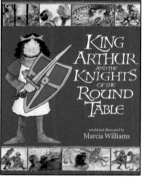

ISBN 978-1-4063-0348-3

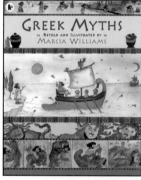

ISBN 978-1-4063-0347-6

ISBN 978-1-4063-0171-7

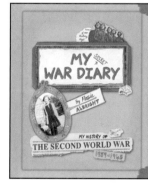

ISBN 978-1-4063-0940-9

ISBN 978-1-4063-1002-3

Available from all good booksellers

www.walker.co.uk